BADLANDS
10 YEARS OF TITTERS

by

Edited by DEBORAH McGARRY

Published By

Pedigree
BOOKS

Pedigree Books Limited, The Old Rectory, Matford Lane, Exeter, Devon EX2 4PS.

ISBN 1.874507.64.3
Printed in Italy.

£6.99
BL2

Panel 1: SOMEONE HAS LEFT THIS MAN OUT HERE TO DIE. THE CRUEL SUN IS STRONG – HE MUST BE VERY CLOSE TO DEATH.

Panel 2: HIS LIFE COULD DEPEND ON JUST A FEW DROPS OF THE DESERT'S MOST PRECIOUS LIQUID.

Panel 3: HEY! WANNA BUY A BOTTLE OF SUNTAN LOTION?

Shown above: The very first BADLANDS strip, May 29, 1989.

BADLANDS debuted in **THE SUN** on Monday, May 29, 1989, having originally appeared in **EDDIE SHAH'S** short-lived newspaper **THE POST.** In those early weeks, the strip ran in black & white and the original artwork was delivered by courier to **THE SUN'S** Wapping offices from **STEVE'S** home in California – a process that could take 2 or 3 days. Over the years, the production and delivery methods have changed as radically as the look of the strip's characters! In the mid-1990s, **STEVE McGARRY** became the first British daily newspaper cartoonist to use computers to colour and deliver his cartoon strips electronically. Each morning, he draws his cartoon by hand, scans the art into a Macintosh computer, adds the colours and then transmits the resulting file by modem directly into **THE SUN's** computers in London – a 6,000 mile journey in a matter of seconds!

BURP!

SCRATCH! SCRATCH!

It's common for the look of comic strip characters to evolve over the years ... these shots of **MARSHAL MASK** demonstrate that the **BADLANDS** crew are no exceptions!

... *MISS BELLE BOTTOM !*

I HAVE HEARD OF YOU, MARSHALL MASK! MY PEOPLE USE SIGN LANGUAGE TO SPEAK YOUR NAME!

987

HERE – LET ME SHOW YOU!

YES – I'M SURE THAT'S ABSOLUTELY FASCINATING...

NOW, IF YOU DON'T MIND PULLING YOUR TROUSERS BACK UP...

CHANGES!

A quick look at how much the rest of the **BADLANDS** characters have changed in the past ten years ...

Your average western hero is courageous, honest, bold and true ... but **MARSHAL MASK** is not your average western hero! The masked moron has set new standards in meddling, muddling, moaning and malingering ...

This stumbling, bumbling buffoon-with-a-badge has turned the town of **BADLANDS** into **DODGE CITY** ... by spending every waking hour dodging danger, dodging hard work and dodging the amorous advances of **BELLE BOTTOM** !

MARSHAL MASK

819

MARSHAL MASK

MARSHAL MASK

MARSHAL MASK

MARSHAL MASK

MARSHAL MASK

MARSHAL MASK

MARSHAL MASK

MARSHAL MASK

MARSHAL MASK

235

236

237

MARSHAL MASK

MARSHAL MASK

MARSHAL MASK

MARSHAL MASK

MARSHAL MASK

Groan! OLD FRIENDS... Cough! THANK YOU ALL FOR COMING...

PROMISE ME YOU'LL REMEMBER ONLY THE GOOD TIMES...

WE HAD JOY, WE HAD FUN, WE HAD SEASONS IN THE SUN...

OH, FOR PITY'S SAKE, MAN... IT'S ONLY AN *INGROWN TOENAIL!!!*

I SEE A WHITE LIGHT... OOERR... IS THAT YOU, MOTHER?

540

WHAT CAUSES AN *INGROWN TOENAIL?*

THE DOCTOR THINKS MY BOOTS ARE PROBABLY TOO TIGHT...

THEY ARE RESTRICTING THE NORMAL GROWTH PROCESS...

INTERESTING THEORY... DID HE HAPPEN TO MENTION ANYTHING ABOUT YOUR TROUSERS?

I THOUGHT YOU WERE HERE TO CHEER ME UP...

541

HOW DID THE *INGROWN TOENAIL* OPERATION GO?

NOT TOO BAD...

...BUT THE DOC GAVE ME LOTS OF GRIEF ABOUT MY *FOOT HYGIENE!*

AH! TAKE NO NOTICE OF THAT CODSWALLOP... THEY GAVE ME THOSE LECTURES WHEN I HAD *MY FOOT OPERATION!*

WHAT WERE YOU IN FOR, *WILLIE?* INGROWN TOENAILS? BUNIONS?

NO... I HAD TO HAVE MY SOCKS SURGICALLY REMOVED...

545

MARSHAL MASK

MARSHAL MASK

MARSHAL MASK

MARSHAL MASK

As forceful and resourceful as his partner is clueless and gormless, perhaps it's a sense of duty ... perhaps it's a sense of pity ... perhaps it's just a warped sense of humour ... but SOMETHING keeps **PONGO** by **MARSHAL MASK's** side!

With his iron physique and his steel-trap mind, this mighty warrior boasts an intellect that is as razor-sharp as his tongue! **PONGO** brings the brains and the brawn to the partnership and **MARSHAL MASK** brings ... erm, well ... the badge?

P·O·N·G·O

I'M BEGINNING TO FEEL I CAN NO LONGER WEAR THE SACRED FEATHER...

I'VE OFTEN WONDERED ABOUT THAT FEATHER, *PONGO*...

DO YOU WEAR IT ON RELIGIOUS GROUNDS? IS IT SOME SORT OF HOLY TRIBAL CUSTOM?

I THOUGHT IT MADE ME LOOK TALLER...

PONGO

265

266

267

PONGO

PONGO

P.O.N.G.O

PONGO

P·O·N·G·O

PONGO

P·O·N·G·O

PONGO

480

PERHAPS THE TIME HAS COME WHEN I CAN NO LONGER WEAR THE SACRED FEATHER!

WOW! IS THIS LIKE SOME SORT OF HOLY RITUAL?

A MYSTIC RITE THAT A WARRIOR MUST ENDURE AS HE REACHES A SPIRITUAL PLATEAU?

ERR...NO... I CAN'T GET A *BASEBALL CAP* TO FIT ME...

484

I AGONISE OVER WHETHER OR NOT TO WEAR THE *SACRED FEATHER*...

YOU POOR TORTURED SOUL...

ON THE ONE HAND, I AM VERY MINDFUL OF THE SYMBOLISM... THE HERITAGE... THE TRADITIONS SWIRLING BACK THROUGH THE MISTS OF TIME...

ON THE OTHER HAND...

... I THINK IT MAKES ME LOOK LIKE A BIT OF A DIVVY...

STILL GOT THE FEATHER, EH?

YES... I TOOK SOME ADVICE FROM A FRIEND...

... *WISE* ADVICE FROM A *TRUSTED* FRIEND!

WHO DO YOU KNOW WHO IS *WISE* AND *TRUSTED*?

LET'S JUST SAY THIS *WISE, TRUSTED FRIEND* WEARS A *MASK* AND *WHITE GLOVES*...

IS IT *MICHAEL JACKSON*?

485

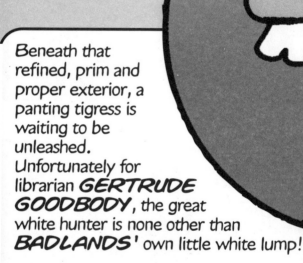

Beneath that refined, prim and proper exterior, a panting tigress is waiting to be unleashed. Unfortunately for librarian **GERTRUDE GOODBODY**, the great white hunter is none other than **BADLANDS'** own little white lump!

WILDERNESS WILLIE has met the woman of his dreams - which explains why the poor old soul keeps nodding off before he can get to grips with the object of his desires! A lonely intellectual and a loony little Lothario ... who said romance was dead?

GERTRUDE GOODBODY

GERTRUDE GOODBODY

175 STEVE McGARRY

176 STEVE McGARRY

177 STEVE McGARRY

GERTRUDE GOODBODY

GERTRUDE GOODBODY

184

185

186

GERTRUDE GOODBODY

GERTRUDE GOODBODY

GERTRUDE GOODBODY

GERTRUDE GOODBODY

WHAT'S IT TO BE?

WHAT CAN YOU RECOMMEND FOR A VEGETARIAN?

HOW ABOUT A DELICATE BLEND OF TOMATOES, VINEGAR, SUGAR AND SPICES, WHIPPED INTO A THICK SAUCE...

... SERVED AT ROOM TEMPERATURE ON A HAND-CARVED SLAB OF FRESH-BAKED, GRANARY GOODNESS?

YOU MEAN "KETCHUP ON A SLICE OF BREAD"?

399   STEVE McGARRY

WHAT DO YOU THINK OF THE PLACE?

IT'S A DUMP!

HEY! I HEARD THAT!

I'LL HAVE YOU KNOW THIS IS A FOUR STAR RESTAURANT!

IS HE TALKING ABOUT ITS RATING IN THE "GOOD FOOD GUIDE"?

NO... HE'S PROBABLY TALKING ABOUT HOW THE WINE TASTES LIKE PETROL...

400   STEVE McGARRY

LET'S GET OUT OF THIS DUMP!

THANKS FOR YOUR CUSTOM — PLEASE COME AGAIN!

ARE YOU MAD? I WOULDN'T BE SURPRISED IF THIS MEAL GIVES US FOOD POISONING!

WELL, IF IT DOES, JUST BRING IN A DOCTOR'S NOTE AND I'LL GIVE YOU A 10% DISCOUNT NEXT TIME!

DAMN FAIR! CAN'T ARGUE WITH THAT!!!

STEVE McGARRY 401

GERTRUDE GOODBODY

GERTRUDE GOODBODY

GERTRUDE GOODBODY

GERTRUDE GOODBODY

GERTRUDE GOODBODY

GERTRUDE GOODBODY

GERTRUDE GOODBODY

BAR BELLE'S lusty landlady is determined to bestow her bounteous charms on **MARSHAL MASK.** She spends her days trying to manhandle him up the aisle ... and her evenings trying to manhandle him, plain-and-simple!

Having abandoned all hope of ever finding "Mr. Right," **BELLE BOTTOM** has settled for giving herself to "Mr. Right-Here-and-Now" ... and there is certainly a lot to give! It's close combat in the battle of the sexes ... and war is always hel!l

BELLE BOTTOM

Tee-Hee! DO YOU REMEMBER THIS? "EYE..." "NOSE..."

"CHEEKY... CHEEKY... CHIN!"

ERR...AND "CHIN..." "CHIN..." ANOTHER "CHIN..."

SMACK!

OH..."TSK! TSK!"

"CHEEKY, CHEEKY, FIST..."

Sob!

SSI LUKE & STEVE McGARRY

BELLE BOTTOM

BELLE BOTTOM

BELLE BOTTOM

BELLE BOTTOM

BELLE BOTTOM

B.E.L.L.E. BOTTOM

BELLE BOTTOM

BELLE BOTTOM

OOH! CUTE! I'D LOOK GOOD IN SOMETHING LIKE THAT!

ERR...YES, DEAR...

IF WE PLAY *PIRATES* YOU CAN USE IT AS AN *EYEPATCH*...

602

Steve McGarry

IT'S REALLY DIFFICULT TO FIND A BRA TO FIT ME...

I NEVER KNOW WHAT CUP SIZE I AM...

YOU'VE SEEN ME NAKED - WHAT DO YOU THINK? AM I A "*DD CUP*..." OR MAYBE AN "*EE CUP*"...

TO TELL YOU THE TRUTH, *BELLE*... I THINK EACH ONE OF THOSE RASCALS...

... COULD FILL THE "*F.A. CUP*"...

603

Steve McGarry

MARSHAL! WHAT ARE YOU DOING IN A *LINGERIE* SHOP?

I'M HERE WITH *BELLE*...

SHE'S IN THE CUBICLE TRYING ON A *TUMMY-FLATTENING, BREAST-LIFTING, THIGH-SHAPING ALL-IN-ONE BODY SUIT*...

HERE SHE IS N-'- EEK!

AAAGH! ALL THAT SURPLUS FLESH... HER HEAD IS SWELLING...

FOR PITY'S SAKE *GERTRUDE*... GET ME SCISSORS...

ANY SECOND NOW...SHE'S *GONNA BLOW!!!*

604 Steve McGarry

BELLE BOTTOM

BELLE BOTTOM

BELLE BOTTOM

In genteel circles, British thespian **SIR CRISPIN DRY** would be hailed as a *"bon vivant"* who is merely *"resting between engagements"* ... unfortunately, he no longer moves in those circles and the rabble at **BAR BELLE** have pegged him as a lazy lush!

These days the blue blood may be 80% proof but the aristocratic actor can still turn in an inspired performance when he wants to ... especially when he's trying to devise new ways of getting some unsuspecting innocent to buy him a large brandy or two!

SIR CRISPIN DRY

SIR CRISPIN DRY

SIR CRISPIN DRY

SIR CRISPIN DRY

SIR CRISPIN DRY

151

153

SIR CRISPIN DRY

SIR CRISPIN DRY

SIR CRISPIN DRY

WHAT THE HELL ARE WE DOING OUT HERE IN THE MIDDLE OF NOWHERE?

YOU'VE GOT TO LEARN TO LOVE THE **GREAT OUTDOORS!**

I PREFER THE GREAT **INDOORS** — ESPECIALLY DURING LICENSING HOURS!

NATURE IS FASCINATING — LOOK AT THESE **HOPS**, FOR INSTANCE...

HOPS ARE USED TO BREW BEER... IT'S A LONG COMPLICATED PROCESS...

LET'S JUST **SKIP** THE **HOPS** AND **JUMP** STRAIGHT TO **BEER** — WHERE'S THE NEAREST BOOZER?

SLAP!

531

I **DON'T** BELIEVE IT... **YOU** OF ALL PEOPLE!

FANCY **YOU** GETTING AN ALLOTMENT!

I'VE SEEN THE LIGHT, **WILLIAM**... RECOGNISED THE BEAUTY OF NATURE!

MIND YOU... YOU'LL HAVE TO DO SOMETHING ABOUT ALL THESE **WEEDS**...

DANDELION WINE... NETTLE BEER...

THESE AREN'T **WEEDS**, MAN... THESE ARE MY **BABIES!!!**

532

I HEAR YOU'VE GOT YOURSELF A LITTLE ALLOTMENT?

YES... I'M GOING TO GROW MY OWN **VEGETABLES** AND **WEEDS**...

I DISCOVERED YOU CAN USE THEM TO MAKE **BEER** AND **WINE!**

I'VE GOT A HORSE — I CAN GET YOU LOADS OF **MANURE!**

ERR... NO OFFENSE...

...BUT I THINK I'D RATHER STICK TO **FLAVOURS** I KNOW!

533

SIR CRISPIN DRY

Growing old disgracefully, this lecherous little Lothario has gradually lost all his inhibitions ... along with his teeth, his hair and most of his marbles! A living legend ... unfortunately, the legend is the one that goes "there's no fool like an old fool!"

What he lacks in certain departments ... height and hygiene spring readily to mind ... **WILDERNESS WILLIE** makes up for with a lust for life that would shame most men half his age and twice his size. Mind you, most men ARE half his age and twice his size!

WILDERNESS WILLIE

WILDERNESS WILLIE

WILDERNESS WILLIE

WILDERNESS WILLIE

WILDERNESS WILLIE

WILDERNESS WILLIE

WILDERNESS WILLIE

WILDERNESS WILLIE

WILDERNESS WILLIE

WILDERNESS WILLIE

WILDERNESS WILLIE

WILDERNESS WILLIE

WILDERNESS WILLIE

WILDERNESS WILLIE

WILDERNESS WILLIE

WILDERNESS WILLIE

WILDERNESS WILLIE

HAPPY BADLANDS

HALLOWEEN

HAPPY BADLANDS

CHRISTMAS

10 THiNGS YOU NeVeR KNeW

1. *STEVE McGARRY* was born in Manchester, on the sprawling Wythenshawe council estate, on January 24, 1953. The eldest of three brothers, his first school was Saints John Fisher and Thomas Moore in Benchill. He later attended St.Bede's R.C. College, in the same year as fellow *MANCHESTER CITY* fanatic and future *JOY DIVISION/NEW ORDER* manager, *FACTORY RECORDS* founder *ROB GRETTON*.

2. At 14, *STEVE* lied about his age to land a weekend job selling raffle tickets at *MANCHESTER CITY's* home games. Not only did he get paid, he got to sit on a touchline bench for all the club's games and could regularly be seen posing for the TV cameras whenever the action strayed towards his position. (Years later he had his own cartoon series in the *MANCHESTER CITY* match-day programme - mainly so he could blag free tickets!)

3. In 1977, a rush of blood to the head saw him quit his job in the catalogue production department of *GREAT UNIVERSAL STORES* mail order company to try his luck as a full-time freelancer. His first published works were illustrations in the now-defunct girl's comic *ROMEO*.

4. In the late '70s, *STEVE* designed ("very badly," he cheerfully confesses) record sleeves for a host of Mancunian punk-rock luminaries, including *JOY DIVISION, JILTED JOHN, SLAUGHTER & THE DOGS, JOHN COOPER CLARKE* and the fabulously-monikered *ED BANGER AND THE NOSEBLEEDS.* He was also the in-house poster/flyer designer for legendary Manchester rock venue *RAFTERS.* Promoted by the great Northern cabaret superstar *DOUGIE JAMES,* the venue played host to fledglings like *ELVIS COSTELLO, DIRE STRAITS, THE POLICE, WHITESNAKE* and *XTC.* (*ROB GRETTON* was the house deejay and it was at *RAFTERS* that he struck up a rapport with *WARSAW* and offered to manage them. Soon after, the group changed their name to *JOY DIVISION.*)

5. *STEVE* was once a partner in a commercial production company and sang on tv and radio ads for for the likes of *TIMPSON'S SHOES.* His finest hour was undoubtedly a *POPNUT CRUNCH POPCORN* animated tv commercial, for which he multi-tracked the voices of a boy, a bear, a rabbit and a python singing *"If you're crazy over popcorn here's a nuttier way to munch, It's peanut-coated popcorn and they call it Popnut Crunch!"*

ABOUT Steve McGarry

6. Childhood piano lessons were followed, in his teens, by the acquisition of his first guitar. *STEVE's* pop career spluttered to a grinding halt on the Northern England cabaret circuit ... but among the members of *STEVE McGARRY'S FIRST OFFENCE* who progressed a little further were *DONALD JOHNSON* of *A CERTAIN RATIO* and *TOBY TOMAN,* who later enjoyed international chart success with *PRIMAL SCREAM.*

7. As none of *STEVE's* musical adventures ever made any money, he was fortunate that girlfriend *DEBS* (pictured left with *STEVE* in *FIRST OFFENCE*) was in regular employment and able to keep him in the lager-guzzling manner to which he had become accustomed. The two met in 1977 and were married in 1984. Twin sons were born three years later, *JOSEPH POWER* arriving just before midnight on October 10th and *LUKE EDWARD* following 45 minutes later on October 11th.

Left to right: Joe, Debs, Steve and Luke, Huntington Beach, California, November, 1998

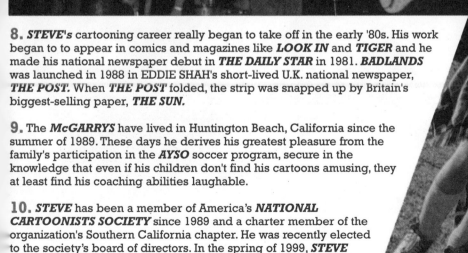

8. *STEVE's* cartooning career really began to take off in the early '80s. His work began to to appear in comics and magazines like *LOOK IN* and *TIGER* and he made his national newspaper debut in *THE DAILY STAR* in 1981. *BADLANDS* was launched in 1988 in EDDIE SHAH's short-lived U.K. national newspaper, *THE POST.* When *THE POST* folded, the strip was snapped up by Britain's biggest-selling paper, *THE SUN.*

9. The *McGARRYS* have lived in Huntington Beach, California since the summer of 1989. These days he derives his greatest pleasure from the family's participation in the *AYSO* soccer program, secure in the knowledge that even if his children don't find his cartoons amusing, they at least find his coaching abilities laughable.

10. *STEVE* has been a member of America's *NATIONAL CARTOONISTS SOCIETY* since 1989 and a charter member of the organization's Southern California chapter. He was recently elected to the society's board of directors. In the spring of 1999, *STEVE McGARRY* was nominated for a *REUBEN* award - the cartooning world's equivalent of the *OSCARS* - as *NEWSPAPER ILLUSTRATOR OF THE YEAR.*